Suniti Namjoshi was born in India in 1941. She has worked as an Officer in the Indian Administrative Service and in academic posts in India and Canada. Since 1972 she has taught in the Department of English of the University of Toronto and has recently spent time living and writing in Devon.

She has published numerous poems, fables, articles and reviews in anthologies, collections and literary and Women's Studies journals in India, Canada, the U.S. and Britain. She has published five books of poetry in India and two in Canada, *The Authentic Lie*, 1982, and *From the Bedside Book of Nightmares*, 1984. Her first book of fiction, *Feminist Fables*, was published by Sheba Feminist Publishers in 1981; her second, *The Conversations of Cow*, by The Women's Press in 1985; and her third, *Aditi and the one-eyed monkey*, written for children, by Sheba Feminist Publishers in 1986. With Gillian Hanscombe she has written the sequence of poems *Flesh and Paper*, published in 1986 by Ragweed in Canada and in both book and audio cassette form by Jezebel Tapes and Books in Britain.

SUNITI NAMJOSHI

THE
BLUE
DONKEY
FABLES

 The Women's Press

Published by the Women's Press Limited 1988
A member of the Namara Group
34 Great Sutton Street, London EC1V 0DX

British Library Cataloguing in Publication Data is available

Typeset by Boldface Typesetters, London EC1
Printed and bound in Great Britain by
Hazell Watson & Viney Ltd, Aylesbury, Bucks

This book is for Gillian Hanscombe, whose poem 'Sometimes seeing is l/ike daffodils or lilac' prefaces this collection.

Sometimes seeing is l/ike
daffodils or lilac
                    (first you see them then you don't)
accepting the bleak of weather
                    (stems bald or just beheaded)
as if a single flame, a singular flower
can justify the rooting underground
(in atonement for light);

and the creatures (sound
echoing sense,
                    booming and blooming both) p/resent
(is it?) an unequal match,
                    indifferent by natural virtue,
to changing a point of view. (It's the shift of tone,
the tense of touch, gives such emphasis
to flowers, beasts

unlikely landscapes;   seen
is not seeing.)
                    (If they could choose, they'd rather
                                        be used
than be eaten, rather be metaphors)
                    and any gigantic flower
is, after all, a need in the eye of the beholder.
Sometimes seeing is like daffodils or lilac
in atonement for light.

Gillian Hanscombe

Acknowledgments

I would like to thank the Canada Council, Christine Donald, Ann Boddington and Sue Gilbert for their help.

Some of the poems and fables have appeared previously in the following anthologies: *A Double Colonization*, *Ain't I a Woman*, *Beautiful Barbarians*, *Charting the Journey*, *Dykeversions* and *Women and Words*; and in the following magazines and journals: *Canadian Literature*, *Canadian Woman Studies*, *Descant*, *Kunapipi*, *Manushi*, *New Statesman*, *Pink Ink*, *Poetry Canada Review*, *Revue Trois*, *Rites* and *Toronto South Asia Review*.

Contents

The Blue Donkey

Marc Chagall, *The Blue Donkey*

Once upon a time a blue donkey lived by a red bridge. 'Inartistic,' said the councillors who governed that town. 'A donkey who lives by our bright red bridge must be of the purest and silkiest white or we must request that the said donkey be required to move on.' The matter soon turned into a political issue. One party said that donkeys never had been and never would be white and what was asked of the donkey was grossly unfair. If, on the other hand, the donkey were required to be a nondescript grey (instead of a loud and laughable blue), they would be prepared to accept the solution as a reasonable way out. But the opposing party found a fault in their logic. 'Just because donkeys have never been known to be white,' they pointed out patiently, 'it does not follow that a donkey is incapable of achieving whiteness. Your argument imposes an arbitrary limitation on the creature's potential.' 'Good heavens!' cried the others. 'Are you suggesting that the donkey's blueness may be a matter of culpable wilfulness rather than a mere genetic mischance?' 'Yes,' responded the logicians. 'Let us confront the creature and you can see for yourselves.'

They approached the donkey, who happened to be munching a bright pink carrot which clashed most horribly with the bright red bridge. 'O Donkey,' they said, feeling they had better get it over with at once, 'we'd like you to turn an inoffensive grey or else move on.' 'Can't and won't,' replied the donkey. 'There you see,' cried half the populace. 'Obviously wilful!' 'No, no,' cried the other half. 'Patently flawed!' And they began to dispute among themselves. The donkey was puzzled. 'I'm a perfectly good donkey,' she said at last. 'What exactly is the matter with you?' 'Your blueness troubles us,' wailed the citizens. 'It clashes with our bridge, as does the pinkness of your carrots. Oh what shall we do? We cannot agree among ourselves.' 'Look again,' advised the donkey.

1

And so they did; they looked and argued and squabbled and argued and after a while most of them got used to the blueness of the donkey and didn't notice it any more. But a few remained who maintained strongly that blueness was inherent, and a few protested that it was essentially intentional. And there were still a few others who managed to see – though only some-times – that the Blue Donkey was only herself and therefore beautiful. These last occasionally brought her a bunch of blue flowers which she put in a vase.

Apotheosis

It so happened that in her middle years the Blue Donkey acquired a certain fame. The townsfolk grew quite proud of her. She attracted tourists. Blue Donkey bars and bistros sprouted, and there was a brisk trade in trinkets, T-shirts and Blue Donkey toys. She herself was installed in a stable and in order to see her it became necessary to buy tickets.

At first the Blue Donkey enjoyed the attention, then she grew bored, and then she took to questioning the tourists. 'Why?' she would ask them. 'Why do you come from near and far merely to see me?' The tourists were delighted. 'Because,' they told her, gawping happily, 'because, O Blue and Beautiful One, we admire you so. Your fame has travelled on the four winds.' She felt pleased. It was nice to be famous. And when the tourists pleaded for a snippet of her rare fur, she allowed them to snip and chop as they wished. Soon she began to look scruffy. The townsfolk worried. They shut down the stable and begged her to grow her fur quickly. The Blue Donkey obliged, and then they discovered that her fur had turned a beautiful grey. They were horrified. 'Oh what shall we do?' Someone suggested a blue pane of glass, but the donkey brushed such suggestions aside.

'I am retiring,' she told them firmly.

'But what about us? What can we possibly tell the tourists?' wailed the townsfolk.

'Tell them the truth. Tell them that I have become a legend,' she replied grandly.

'But will it work?' They still looked anxious.

'Of course,' she assured them. 'Truth is dazzling.'

Curtain

Once the Blue Donkey had retired gracefully, it became necessary to substitute a legend. And for the legend to be efficacious, it became necessary to spread a rumour. The townsfolk went to work with a will. 'The Blue Donkey is with us no more,' they whispered to the tourists. They looked mournful. Some went so far as to hold a funeral. This was too much. The Blue Donkey summoned the mayor. 'I may be getting on, and I may be grey; but I am not dead. The gossip about me is more than malicious. Who is responsible?' 'Oh, well, um, ah, we are,' replied the mayor. 'In order to make your legend prosper, we had to kill you off, you know.' The Blue Donkey was very angry. She threatened to disclose the truth to the world. 'Oh, please don't. The tourists would claim we had perpetrated a fraud. Indeed, some might say you were fraudulent. Oh please, please.' The mayor pleaded and pleaded with her, and at last she agreed to think it over.

The Blue Donkey spent a difficult night, but in the morning she was resolute. She still felt that the truth must be told. Accordingly, she walked through the city and proclaimed loudly that the Blue Donkey had never died, only changed colour. People were thunderstruck. Some doubted her, some believed. A sect was formed called the Neo-Resurrectionists. Their colours were a militant grey on a field of azure; their motto, 'Truth is stranger . . . ' Soon there were streetfights, headlines in the papers, heated debates in learned journals. The Blue Donkey was a little surprised, but she had done her duty and once again she gracefully retired. As for the mayor and the townsfolk, they were beside themselves with joy. The intake of tourists had more than doubled.

Last Word

During her retirement it somehow came about that the Blue Donkey took to telling lies. She slipped into it gradually. And her motives – well, her motives were obscure. Some of it was weariness. She found that in spite of all her efforts her friends heard what they wished to hear. For example, half of them were certain that the Blue Donkey had tired of fame and success and the glitter of publicity and had retired to the country to purify her soul. The other half were convinced that the Blue Donkey had been battered by the world and had sought refuge in obscurity to lick her wounds. She had tried to explain that both these versions were inexact, but it had made little difference. Half her friends applauded her modesty, and the other half smiled and nodded and winked knowingly.

It may be argued that as a motive for lying, weariness of itself is hardly sufficient; and it's true there were other factors. One of these was complaisance. When youngsters begged her for the truth about one of her legendary exploits, she felt in her heart that a flat refusal was hardly the answer. And yet, to fail to tell the truth is not quite the same thing as an outright lie. An inarguable lie requires, as it were, some justification. The Blue Donkey felt this herself. She took time and trouble. She learnt to embroider with endless patience; and, it must be admitted, she acquired a certain cunning. She confined her lies to her own experience, and devoted disciples wrote them all down. So that it would be difficult to convict her of 'lying' as such, were it not for the fact that the published text states resolutely that any resemblances are pure coincidence. It – how should one phrase it? – at the very least, it makes one wonder.

Explanation

(i) No Daffodil

Why do you write about plants and animals?
                        Why not people?

Because
        no daffodil shrieks to be plucked,
                no lily rages, 'Admire my bower.'
        And if dogs go about and shit
                their shit, at least it mixes
                with the stones and mud.
Somebody screeches that the trees
        have scattered their leaves in her garden.
O untidy trees, O vexing dogs,
        but they do not enter the house to be fed,
        they make no work, to which she says,
        'That is not true.' And, of course,
        there is a sense in which it is not.
But if ordinary people would behave like trees,
        or like cats and dogs, or better still
        like the wilder animals, then I could admit
        a dispassionate liking for each one of them,
        the ugly and ignoble, the squat and the tall.
Someone explains,
        'A tree is not a person. A boy is not a cat.'
'Yes,' I reply, striving for patience,
        'that is the problem. Precisely that.'

(ii) Lions

Well, let's tell the truth.
        The cat charmed me.
         The tree disarmed me
And though the real people
           hadn't yet harmed me,
I thought that they would
          given the chance.
'Control your emotions,'
         the grown-ups had said.
'If any insult you,
        avert your head.'
But the message got muddled.
     I cowered from the crowd, and fed
            lions instead.

(iii) A Difference

'But surely,' she says, 'there are some
        you love, some you trust?
Me, for example. Think of me
        please as some sort of flower.'
It's easy enough. We're sitting
         on the grass.
She looks exactly
       like a gigantic flower.
So I say so to her,
       but she still looks sad.
'There is a difference,'
        she tells me gently,
'between a simile
      and a genuine metaphor.'

(iv) Cornered

'Yes, but cats eat birds.'
           I am not devastated.
I shrug in reply,
                'Animals eat.'
'Yes, but well-fed cats
              with larders stocked
with tins of cat food
              go out and eat.'
I see a coterie of well-groomed
                    cats
who go out to dine in the late
                    evenings.
I try not to smile.
          'Why are you smiling?'
Time to be honest. 'Because,
              I suppose,
they don't eat me.'
          She is not satisfied.
'Cats are sadists.' I had half
            thought of that.
'Oh no', I say. 'Cats are like
             children.
They play with their food ...'
             With that
she pounces.
          'But you think
that people are childish
        and that the human child
is particularly horrid.'
         Cornered at last,
'Cats,' I murmur, I murmur feebly,
        'Cats agree with me.'

The One-eyed Monkey Goes into Print

It was winter. The sun was shining like anything. It was pleasant, it was cool. The temperature was about seventy degrees. The one-eyed monkey was feeling mellow and middle aged. 'I have travelled,' she said. 'I have seen the world. I have lost my tail, six of my teeth and one eye. I have lived. It's time I wrote down what I think about it.' But her friends, the crocodiles, appeared not to have heard.

'Ahem,' she said loudly. 'I'm going to write a book.'

'What for?' murmured one crocodile and went on dozing.

'What about?' muttered the other crocodile and went on basking.

She ignored the first crocodile and addressed the second exclusively.

'About me,' she said strongly.

'Oh,' replied the crocodile. 'Will I be in it?'

'Well, I don't know,' she answered. 'Why would a book about monkeys have crocodiles in it?' But she saw that his eyes were beginning to close, so she added quickly, 'But I'll put you in it.'

'Me as I am?' he asked, stretching out his tail luxuriously.

'No, you as you are in relation to me.'

'Oh.' He sounded dubious.

'And you have to help me,' she put in quickly.

'Help you to write it?' He sounded interested.

'No, no, I can do that. To tell you the truth I've already done it. I want you to help me get it published.'

'Oh.' He thought for a moment. 'Well, I have some contacts with the animal rights people. Send it to them and see what they think.'

So she wrote to them and they wrote back that her title was lacking in human interest. That's what makes a book sell. People are interested in people, you know, they pointed out perfectly pleasantly. But they enclosed the addresses of a few publishers who were non-mainstream.

The one-eyed monkey had a crisis of conscience. Should she change the title? She changed it. It had been called *The Life and Leanings of a One-eyed Monkey*. She went through the text. Wherever the word 'monkey' appeared she put in 'blank'. *The Life and Leanings of a One-eyed Blank*. She said it out loud. She persuaded herself that it had a ring to it. 'I speak in parables,' she told herself bravely. 'The intelligent will know how to read in between the blanks and will appreciate my true, my native, my deliciously malicious monkey wit.'

She sent it off to the publishers. Some wrote back and some misplaced it. Those who wrote back told her bluntly, 'The syntax slithers and the vision is monocular. Who is talking to whom, may we ask? We regret to inform you that your work is entirely lacking in clarity.' The one-eyed monkey felt disheartened. She brooded for days. Then she re-submitted the manuscript with the word 'monkey' typed in clearly. And the miracle happened. A smaller publisher wrote to her saying that they were intrigued by her manuscript and would like to publish it. But please, they begged her to remember that an audience of exclusively one-eyed monkeys was hard to find; could she help to pay for it?

The one-eyed monkey tore her fur in utter despair. Her friends, the crocodiles, happened to notice.

'Oh, all right,' they said. 'We'll help you to rewrite it.'

'But it mustn't be about monkeys and it mustn't be about crocodiles.'

'No,' they agreed. They made suggestions and the monkey rewrote it.

In the end the book achieved a moderate success under the title *The Amorous Adventures of a One-eyed Minx*. 'Is it autobiographical?' the reviewers wondered. 'No,' declared the monkey quite truthfully, 'I do not recognise myself in it.' But her publishers beamed. They patted her back. 'Art transforms,' they murmured kindly.

Poetic Practice

There was once a cat – her name was Suki – who was enthusiastic about snow. 'It's great stuff,' she would say; and her friend, Suniti, who was always polite, agreed with her. But one day Suki went on rather longer than usual. 'There is nothing more soft and simple than snow. Snow is sincere. Snow smiles and smoothes away sorrow.' Suniti couldn't understand it. 'Suki?' she ventured. But Suki interrupted. 'Suki,' she carolled, 'sounds like snow.' 'Well, so does Suniti. So what?' 'So nothing. I'm a sensitive cat, and I'm expressing my sentiments on the subject of snow.' Suniti wondered whether it was wise to go on, but she was worried. 'Suki,' she pointed out, 'it isn't snowing outside. It's brilliant summer.' She received no answer.

That night she went to bed greatly troubled. Had she hurt Suki's feelings? What had the cat been doing? In the end she decided that Suki had been writing a poem about snow, and that she, Suniti, had failed to appreciate it. Apologies were in order.

The following day, when she found Suki with her paw planted on a blank sheet of paper and with her gaze unfocused, she knew she'd been right. 'Suki,' she said, approaching diffidently, 'I'm sorry I was such a stupid simpleton, and so silly as not to see the singularity and sibilance of your Sequence on Snow.' But Suki remained motionless. Not even her ears moved. Suniti was desperate. With a tremendous effort she blurted out suddenly, 'I say, Suki, snow is simply super, you know.' Suki yawned. 'Poems are passé,' she informed Suniti. 'I am concentrating on concrete verse. Here, as you see, is my latest effort.'

Suniti stared at her. 'Is it – is it a Study of a Cat on a Small Field of Snow?'

'No, stupid. I have called it "Poetic Practice". In it I have captured the thing itself, the poet at work. Don't you think it's really rather good?'

11

Suniti looked at Suki again and at the paw resting on the blank piece of paper.

'Oh yes.' She hesitated. 'I see what you mean. I – I think you're wonderful!'

And Suki sighed with relief and satisfaction. 'At last you've understood how poetry works.'

Three Angel Poems

(i) Familiar Angel

Angel sitting on my shoulder
                is cackling loudly.
I tell her, 'This is not wise,
             one might surmise
             that some bawdy bird
             had thus given way
             to absurd mirth.'
Angel shrieks. She claps apart
        her two black wings.
                    She leans
      over backwards.
                    She loses
      her perch. Then
         she digs her claws in.
                She chortles and shrieks.
I mumble, 'My shoulder hurts.'
And Angel croons. She croons in my ear,
            'Poor thing. Oh what a poor, poor,
                    very poor thing.'
I mutter, 'That's not what I mean.'
Angel smirks. 'O happy Angel. Smug Angel.
          Beautiful, Delightful and Delighted Angel,'
Angel sings. Angel grins. Angel fluffs out her feathers
and preens.
         And a voice declares,
'Game and set and match to Angel.'
                Angel wins.

(ii) Visiting Angel

Angel, crow, sparrow, sitting on my shoulder and shitting when you please, who are you, Bird? And why have you come to haunt me thus? My left eye brushes feathers. And you're leaning over sideways to nibble my ears. Sometimes I think you like me, Bird. Let us examine the matter. Let us examine this woman wearing this bird. Don't you care how you look? You look unkempt. You look like a most ruffianly bird. And I? Look shy, a little tousled. But we shall have to explain when we meet other people that I am me and we are us. 'How nice,' they will say. 'Do come along and bring your bird.' O Bird, what a team we should make! You and I shall become famous. Can't you envision it? – The Incredible Woman and Her Invisible Bird!

(iii) Unfallen Angel

There are those who have muses that are kind
and gentle, come when called, are glad to be of use.
And they leave when asked; they don't seem to mind.
There are times when poets don't want a muse.
And, unlike Angel, their clothes are pressed,
their manner polite, their gait graceful.
And while it's true that Angel is seldom dressed,
if she were, she would undoubtedly look disgraceful.
Those others never shriek. As for biting,
kicking and fighting, they would think it rude.
Indeed, the only task they really delight in
is making pure poetry out of crude.
And yet, by heav'n, though Angel struts and Angel grins,
she's Angel still. Then who shall say that Angel sins?

14

Mute Swan

Once upon a time a swan lived alone on a remote lake. She was as swanlike and graceful as any other swan, but by reason of her isolation, aided perhaps by a natural reticence, she had never learned to speak at all. She paddled about, she dived occasionally, once in a while she would shake the water from her great wings and take a turn or two through the blue air. She was happy enough. Now it so happened that the Lady of the Lake was inclined to be both kindly and gracious. At first she was content to throw the swan a bit of watercress. The swan was content to dive after it. This seemed to augur well. The Lady of the Lake grew more ambitious. 'I think I'm going to befriend that swan,' she said to herself. 'I shall teach her to speak, give her some lessons in proper elocution.' The lady collected more watercress, added some hyacinths, threw in a few lilies. And after the lady had exhausted her supplies, and after the swan had dived and retrieved them, the lady pointed to her breast and said loudly and firmly and with the utmost precision, 'Friend.' But the swan merely looked at her and did nothing at all. Now the lady was also inclined to be rather impatient. She snatched some cress from the swan's beak and repeated the performance. The swan watched. The third time around the Lady of the Lake was really angry. 'Stupid beast!' she screamed at the swan. But by this time the swan had understood what was required of her. She arched her neck, drew in her breath, then changed her mind and glided off.

The Saint and the Robin

(i)

The saint standing in her garden was overcome
by the beauty and terror of this world.
'O worm,' she said, bending right down, 'no twist
or turn of your writhing body goes unnoticed,'
but the worm dived making no sound. The saint
undaunted spoke to a robin, 'O bird,'
she said, 'pity in your pride all God's creatures,'
but that sleek bird cocked an eye that was so
unpitying that the saint paused. She looked
                                        all about,
then fell on her knees and prayed to a god,
                                who was faceless,
and neither bird nor saint – nor worm in the sod.

(ii)

And once again, the world was stuffed
with an extreme significance –
gods in the bushes, saints in trees,
and standing before her the sleek robin,
                    but she could not love it.
'O bird,' she said, 'I do not love you.'
'Nor I you,' said the bird. 'Acquit
yourself of a superior wisdom, love
whom you can, O you silly saint.
                    There's nothing to it.'

16

(iii)

The saint approached. Robin and worm
heaved a great sigh. But the saint
didn't notice. She had cast aside
her earthly pretensions. Robin and worm
were as nothing to her. She watched the sky.
And the sky was a flawless and brilliant blue.
At last it opened. Robin cheered,
worm applauded, and saint maintained
a sober silence as she drifted by.

Prodigal Pudding

There was once a cat who lived in a house and was loved by her mistress, but only on Mondays. Love had been rationed. The mistress of the cat believed in moderation. But the cat herself remained unconvinced. 'O Mistress,' she said, 'O Purveyor of All Pleasures, O Sole Source of Solace and Delight.' 'What?' asked the mistress. 'Well,' said the cat, 'O Sole Source of Salmon and Suchlike, Mondays are good, but the other days are wretched. Nobody can live on Mondays alone.' 'Are you complaining?' enquired the mistress. 'Oh no,' said the cat, 'but there used to be a time when you loved me on Tuesdays and Wednesdays and frequently on Thursdays.' 'Very well,' said the mistress, 'I shall consider the matter. But today is a Tuesday you must understand.' So the cat went away. The next morning the mistress of the cat greeted the cat with the following words: 'O Pudding, O Cat, O Delectable Dish, O My Precocious Piglet and My Heart's Delight, good morning.' 'What happened?' asked the cat. 'Well,' said the mistress, 'I love you so much that in the goodness of my heart I have decided to accede to your request. Since you say that you cannot live on a diet of Mondays, I have decided to give you Wednesdays instead.' The cat went away and thought for a while. Then she came back. 'Thank you,' she said, and they spent the day cooing and clucking and purring and petting and all that. But on Thursday morning the cat wasn't there, nor on Friday. She wasn't there on Saturday or Sunday or Monday or Tuesday. On Wednesday morning the cat reappeared. 'O Prodigal Pudding,' cried the mistress sweetly though she was absolutely furious and wanted to shout, only it was Wednesday, 'where have you been?' 'I've been thinking,' said the cat, 'I see that you're right. One day in seven is more than enough. So I'll see you on Wednesdays and love you then.' 'You can't do that,' roared the mistress. 'Yes, I can,' said the cat, 'and you mustn't roar.' 'But it's outrageous,' said the mistress, 'to have to make do with a Once-a-Week Cat. O Pleasant Pussy Cat,

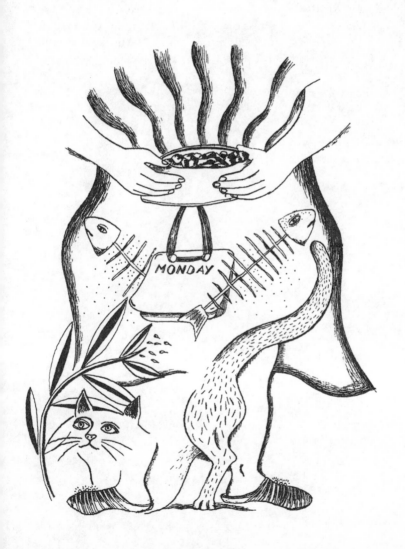

O My Sweet and Generous Darling, won't you reconsider?'
    'Well, all right,' said the cat. 'In future I'll visit you on
Mondays instead.'

Disclaimer

It was someone else,
                someone who died –
not me. It's her you mourn,
                for her
you walk the sad shore,
                and call and cry
most feelingly.
                If she could hear you,
she would surely answer –
                she always did.
And so, she is dead.
                One day
she died
                unaccountably.

20

The Creation: Plan B

One day Parrot said to Tortoise, 'I say, let's make the world.'

'All right,' said Tortoise, 'and let's have continents like the patterns on my back.'

'And lots and lots of parrots,' put in Parrot.

'Ye–es,' said Tortoise, 'and an equal number of tortoises.'

'Of course,' said Parrot.

For a moment or two they contemplated the world they had agreed upon.

'I say,' said Tortoise, breaking the silence, 'do we have to have people?'

'No,' replied Parrot.

'Phew,' said Tortoise.

And they lived happily ever after.

Poem Against Poets

I fall upon the thorns of life,
                    I weep, I bleed,
but to what purpose?
                    There was once a poet
who thought she was a nightingale,
                            and another
who thought she was a rose –
                            charming perhaps,
able certainly, having found at least
                    a way to cope.
Would the nightingale's entrails
                    have been more powerful
(as emblematic objects)
                    laid out on the floor
of a room that you came to, and then
                    withdrew from,
startled and amazed?
                    Oh the rose is bloodless,
she is white with pain;
                    and Philomel wails
in the woods again.
                    But there are the other
more ordinary animals.
            They are not literary.
                    They own their pain.

Interpose an island . . .

Interpose an island in salty seas?
As though we were gods and could create
real places? But islands such as these
we crunch between our teeth, consummate
the wish and the thing made. And then there's this:
we ourselves must still strive, half seen, half hidden,
rolling in troughs, riding the wave, kiss and bliss
the sole measure of what's allowed, what forbidden.
On the islands our bodies are bathed and clean.
An island affords its proper vision
of you – robed and perfumed like some great queen,
out of the reach of roiling confusion.
And yet, it's the swimmer I hold naked and wet
and from whose dear body I lick the salt sweat.

Dusty Distance

One of the stories the Blue Donkey tells – there's a controversy raging about whether to classify it as fact or fiction – is about the first time she set off on a long dusty road to make her fortune. In no time at all she met a woman who offered her a carrot, a place to stay and an occupation. 'No thank you,' replied the Blue Donkey. 'You see, I'm a poet, and I have a long way to go.' 'What is a poet?' enquired the woman. This so disconcerted the Blue Donkey that she muttered and mumbled and managed to utter a hasty goodbye and marched onwards. In consequence she nearly ran down a fellow wayfarer.

The Blue Donkey apologised profusely, and to show that she was genuinely sorry and genuinely interested she asked him who he was and what he was doing and what was his purpose. 'Oh,' he answered sternly, 'I'm on my way to encounter Life. When I find her, I shall take her by the throat and grapple wth her.' 'And then?' asked the Blue Donkey, enthralled by this account in spite of herself. 'And then I shall bind her hand and foot and take her home.' 'And then?' The Blue Donkey was almost whispering now. 'And then,' he responded magnificently, 'I shall chop her up and grind her down and put her into delicate mince pies which shall go on the market at fourpence a dozen.' His teeth were gleaming. He turned on her. 'And who are you?' he enquired suddenly. 'Oh, I'm only a poet,' the Blue Donkey murmured with what she considered suitable modesty. But her fellow traveller grew highly indignant. 'Rubbish!' he cried. 'I am a poet. Why you, you are only a bit of Life.' As he said this his eyes grew round with speculation. The Blue Donkey didn't wait for more. She says that her readers can call her a coward if they like, but she galloped off fast and left him behind in the dusty distance.

Eventually the countryside grew greener. There were landscaped gardens, immaculate woods, and in one of these woods there was a Beautiful Lady reclining gracefully against a convenient tree trunk. She was reading a book. As the Blue Donkey approached, the Lady looked up and smiled at her. 'Hello,' said the Blue Donkey. 'What are you reading?' 'Poetry,' sighed the Lady. 'I think poetry is so beautiful. I feel I could live on poetry and fresh air for ever.' The Blue Donkey edged closer. 'Well, as it happens,' she ventured diffidently, 'I am a poet. Perhaps you would like me to recite some of my verse?' 'Oh. Oh no,' the Lady replied hastily, then she recovered herself. 'The fact is,' she explained, 'that though I have studied many languages and my French and German are both excellent, I have never mastered Blue Donkese. And though I have no doubt whatsoever that your poems are excellent, I fear they would fall on untutored ears.' 'But please, I speak English.' The Blue Donkey could hear herself sounding plaintive. 'Oh,' murmured the Lady. 'But surely as a Blue Donkey, integrity requires that you paint the world as it appears to you. And consider: what have a lady and a donkey in common?'

'Nothing at all,' said the Blue Donkey sadly and she turned away and retraced her steps. At last she came to the door of the woman she had first encountered. 'Please,' she enquired humbly, 'would you settle for a part-time worker for half a carrot?'

The Jacana's Tale

It was still early in the evening, the disciples of the Blue Donkey were gathered about and the Blue Donkey was feeling benevolent; so that when one of the disciples asked eagerly, 'Of all the creatures you have ever met which was the silliest?' and another interrupted, 'No, which was the cleverest?' and a third cried, 'No, no, which was the most modest?' the Blue Donkey paused for a moment and appeared to think before she answered.

'In my youth,' she said, 'I was a great traveller and as I was wandering about the banks of the Ganga I stopped to drink at a bend in the river. The current was rather sluggish at this point and the water had formed a pool. As I nosed my way through the lily pads and the water hyacinths I heard a voice saying, "But just look at your reflection in these waters for a moment. You are the most beautiful creature I've ever seen." Well, I looked. All I saw was my own face, much the same as usual, and then I realised I had made a mistake and I looked again, this time through the reeds. The voice belonged to a small green frog who was earnestly addressing a large jacana. That the frog was caught in the jacana's beak seemed not to disturb either of them. The jacana was straddled across two lily pads and trying to peer into the water. The frog resumed, "If you put me down, you'll be able to see your reflection much better." As soon as the frog was put down, she dived into the water, calling hastily over her shoulder, "I'll just push aside these pads for you." I had watched the scene in complete silence, but now that the frog was quite safe I ventured to say, "That frog is an astute flatterer." The jacana only looked puzzled, then she walked away a few steps and continued to gaze into the water. At last I realised that the jacana hadn't realised what had happened. "How can anyone be taken in so easily!" I was muttering to myself, when I heard the frog whisper, "But look at her. She is beautiful." I looked. It was true.'

The Blue Donkey had stopped talking. The disciples

maintained a respectful silence. Then the boldest of them spoke a little uncertainly. 'Well, obviously the frog was the cleverest and the jaçana was the silliest, but which creature was the most modest?'

'Ah,' replied the Blue Donkey smiling benignly, 'I can't tell you that. But consider, there are at least three creatures in the fable.'

The Disciple

One day a tiger came up to the Blue Donkey and said that she was thirsty for knowledge and would the Blue Donkey please give her some.

'No,' replied the Blue Donkey. 'The sorts of things I have to say are not the sort that tigers learn.'

'Oh please,' pleaded the tiger. 'I don't want to learn tigrish things. It's you I admire and I've come to you for Blue Donkey wisdom.'

'You're mistaken,' replied the Blue Donkey, wishing the tiger would go away because as the tiger grew more and more passionate the Blue Donkey became more and more nervous.

'But I've come all this distance,' insisted the tiger. 'You can't just send me away.'

'Yes I can and I do,' replied the Blue Donkey bravely and turned her back, but the tiger began to follow her about. She was a great nuisance. For one thing she made the Blue Donkey's social life impossible. Friends who dropped by would leave quickly. It was something about the tiger's presence; it altered the very nature and tone of conversation. And yet, the tiger herself never said a word.

Soon the Blue Donkey lost patience. Finding herself alone with the tiger, which was happening increasingly, she turned on her. 'Look. You're ruining my life. Please go.'

'But please,' implored the tiger. 'What have I done?'

'It isn't that so much as who you are, and whom you represent and the effect you achieve,' muttered the Blue Donkey.

'But I've told you who I am,' answered the tiger. 'I am your disciple.'

The Blue Donkey saw she was getting nowhere.

'Very well,' she said. 'Come with me then, as my disciple, and we will go among the tigers and convert the others.'

'Oh no,' cried the tiger drawing back. 'That would be foolish and – and quite impossible.'

'Why?' enquired the Blue Donkey.

'Well, because the tigers would eat you, you know.'

'Oh,' murmured the donkey, 'and what about you? Would they eat you too?'

'Oh no,' said the tiger. 'I am, after all, a fellow tiger.'

'Well then, our course is obvious.'

'Is it?' asked the tiger.

'Yes,' declared the Blue Donkey. 'You are the obvious choice for the Blue Donkey's Deputy Among the Tigers. You must go.'

'What? All by myself?'

'Yes.' The Blue Donkey's answer was heartlessly clear.

So the tiger went. What she achieved is still unknown.

The Three Piglets

It was during the days that the Blue Donkey had retired to the forest for a period of solitude. Early one morning as she was trying to meditate she was approached by three piglets.

'Good morning,' they said, 'We've each of us decided what we're going to be, and on the whole we're sure, but we're not absolutely sure, so we'd like you to give us an aptitude test.' They informed her further that the eldest piglet was going to be a poet, the middle one a saint and the youngest was going into business.

'All right,' said the Blue Donkey, glad to be distracted. 'Now, look at me carefully and tell me, please, what you see.'

'I see Wisdom Incarnate,' declared the eldest piglet, smirking a little because she felt she had delivered a poetic answer. The other two looked abashed. What could they possibly say to equal that?

The second piglet pulled herself together. 'I see a blue donkey,' she answered clearly. Then she shrugged. Well, at least she'd been honest.

It was the youngest one's turn, but she seemed to be undergoing a fit of nerves.

The Blue Donkey spoke to her kindly. 'Why do you want to go into business?'

'To pay the bills.'

The Blue Donkey smiled. 'Well,' she said, 'are you ready to hear the results of the test?'

'No,' protested the first two piglets. 'The littlest one hasn't answered yet.'

'Oh yes, of course.' The Blue Donkey turned to the piglet. 'Well, little one, what do you see?'

The youngest piglet looked at the donkey. 'I see you,' she blurted out suddenly, then she looked at the ground.

'Now,' said the Blue Donkey. 'Are you ready?'

'Yes,' cried the first two piglets. 'Did we pass?'

'You all passed,' replied the Blue Donkey. 'But you've got it a bit wrong.'

'What do you mean?' The poetic piglet was highly indignant.

'You, my friend, ought to go into business – or perhaps into politics,' she added thoughtfully. She turned to the second. 'You, on the other hand, might make a poet. At least you try to describe exactly what you see.'

'But what about her?' They pointed to the youngest. 'Will she make a saint?'

'That I don't know,' answered the donkey. 'Saints are beyond me.'

31

Turf

A frog who lived at the bottom of the garden got a bit above herself. 'This bit of garden is my patch,' she would croak at the cat. 'I have staked it out.' The cat could have walloped the frog easily and sent her flying, but she was a good-natured beast, and so she would just look at the frog and say nothing at all. The frog took her silence to mean assent. The cat didn't care. Frogs were irrelevant. She knew that her real business was with the neighbourhood cats. These she would chase away with a firm growl and when occasion demanded she would fight them. Then she would return to the house to be stroked and admired.

The mistress of the house would stroke and pet her. She knew in her heart that cats were irrelevant, but did not want to disillusion the cat. The cat would then stretch and invite the mistress to do a little gardening, and the mistress, who was a good-natured woman, would thank the cat and sometimes accept.

The three creatures lived happily in this way for quite some time, each thinking that she had an inalienable right to that bit of planet, until it so happened that the master of the house divorced the mistress. No more mistress, no more cat. The frog was delighted. She had had her doubts about whether she could actually drive away the cat; now she felt vindicated.

The Lion Skin

(i)

That in some dream I might be a lion
walking nobly and happily through a wood,
and that some lady, who has had her eye on
me, might say to me I am both great and good.
And then in this dream may this lovely lady
ruffle my yellow mane and trim my claws
and lead me to a spot green and shady,
but here the dream fails. I'm forced to pause.
For what do we say, this lady and I?
What happens next? Do I remove my skin?
And what does she do? Is she shocked and shy?
Or civil, and removes her own clothing?
I've never had the courage to dream the dream through,
but I think she says, 'You be me, and I'll be you.'

(ii)

'Delectable, firm and juicy, such fair flesh
is good to eat.' It was not I who said that,
it was the lady, and I, caught in the mesh
of light and leaves, could only lie there, and let what
might befall, quickly befall me. She took
such pleasure in each simple incision
that, unwilling to betray by a word or look
I felt anything, I admired her precision
as slowly she flayed me. But there's a pleasure
in the nerve ends that makes one want to scream.
At last I screamed. And such was the measure
of this rare lady and such her supreme
and unexampled skill that she made me scream
again and again and long to wake and still to dream.

33

(iii)

Dispense with disguises. The lion's skin
is a skin after all. Spread it on the ground,
so that no twig or stone in this forest clearing
shall hurt or trouble us when we both lie down.
Or should the weather change and we grow cold,
let the fur cover us and warm our sleep
till we wake again and are brave and bold.
And if the stars choose to peep, let them peep.
What can stars or moon or sun discover?
That the lady is a woman, and I,
who lie so close beside her, am her lover?
The stars will not shriek, will make no outcry.
The stars are sensible, and would not sever
woman from woman or lover from lover.

(iv)

I'd been dreaming again and in the dream
everything was lovely. You were very kind.
We'd finished making love and I felt serene.
When suddenly your voice: 'Do you mind
not making love without permission;
I am not the creature of your fantasy.'
I squirmed, I did not know which way to turn
because you were real, at least, real to me.
And so I lied. I said, 'I do not know
who you are. For though you look like her, she
is kind, and her voice gentle, soft and low.
Oh you could not be whom you seem to be.'
You answered, 'No, I am not what I seem.'
With that you vanished and I clutched my dream.

(v)

And yet there's a poetry of penury
that far outdoes the paeans of plenitude,
and the gorgeous dream blooms without injury
only in the hermit's austere solitude.
By which I mean that sometimes my arms ache,
my nostrils twitch, and I feel, or almost feel,
your body's warmth, and then sometimes I fake
the rest, cast caution aside, and make a meal
that would make an emperor look askance.
That I crave, desire and solicit you
is known to us both, and that I may not advance.
And since there is nothing I can say or do,
I tell myself that the dream is made of such stuff
that to dream is best and the dream enough.

(vi)

The thick, tough skin of the lion shall be chopped
and snipped to make six balls, which, when filled with air,
shall go spinning crazily like the lopped
heads of poets crammed with passion and despair.
And you, while walking through the woods some day,
might chance to glance at these leathern orbs
and seize them and make much mirth and holiday.
I shall be content, for the dream that absorbs
me can have no other end. Thus held and seen
it is real, and still real, again and again,
whenever you choose. And what might have been
is cause for contemplation, banishes pain.
Then all shall be well, and by the grace of the muse
this lion skin shall still give pleasure and prove of use.

The Sinner

One afternoon, as the Blue Donkey was reciting some verse before an audience, an ordinary grey donkey marched up to her, fell at her feet and cried out in a loud voice, 'Sister, I have sinned! I seek absolution.' The Blue Donkey was most embarrassed. She bent down and whispered hurriedly, 'Oh do get up. As for sinning, please, that's quite all right.' 'But you don't understand,' the grey donkey moaned. 'You are my sister, and it's against you I have sinned.' Now the Blue Donkey was perfectly sure that the donkey at her feet was not her sister. 'Please,' she said politely, 'there must be some mistake. I am not your sister. Indeed, I don't think we've met. So you see, there's no need to moan. You can't have sinned.' 'Oh yes I have.' The donkey at her feet refused to budge. 'I have been snotty and snobbish and often thought to myself that I despise blue donkeys and would never go near one or have one for a friend.' 'Well there you are.' The Blue Donkey was losing patience. 'That's an excellent reason for removing yourself.' 'But you must listen. I've changed completely,' the grey donkey wailed. 'I believe in sisterhood. I'm going to be your friend.' The Blue Donkey hesitated; there were limits, she decided, even to good manners. 'No,' she replied. 'No. That won't do at all.' 'What? After everything I said? Who exactly do you think you are?' The grey donkey was beside herself. 'Well,' the Blue Donkey soothed, 'you asked for absolution, but you haven't done penance.' 'What must I do?' 'Fall at the feet of the other donkeys here and explain to them – as you did to me – that you excuse their greyness.' 'But – I don't understand.' The Blue Donkey pushed her away. 'Why let that stop you? They, I am sure, will make you understand.'

The Vulgar Streak

The blue jay twittered at the Blue Donkey, 'Birds are better.' The donkey pretended not to have heard. The blue jay went on twittering, 'Birds are better, better, better, much, much better.' The donkey gave up. 'Better than what?' 'Than donkeys,' the jay replied instantly. 'Rubbish!' said the Blue Donkey. 'Not rubbish. Just a fact.' 'Better at what?' asked the Blue Donkey, exasperated in spite of herself. 'Better at flying,' returned the jay. 'But donkeys don't fly.' 'Exactly,' cried the jay on a note of triumph, 'that's my point,' and flapping her wings, she took off.

All that day the Blue Donkey felt disgruntled. She tried to concentrate on important matters, but the jay's remarks kept coming back. When she caught herself wiggling her ears experimentally, she got really cross. 'Well, so what if donkeys can't fly,' she muttered. And she pulled herself together and made an effort and by the following morning she felt all right. But the following morning the jay was back.

'Wouldn't you like to fly?' enquired the jay. Now the Blue Donkey prided herself on being reasonably honest. What could she say? 'Yes,' she said. 'But you can't,' pointed out the jay. 'No,' said the Blue Donkey. 'Too bad.' And the jay took off. All that day the Blue Donkey was in a foul temper. Her friends told her that the blue jay was a flighty fool not in the least worth bothering about, and in any case what did it matter that donkeys couldn't fly. 'I don't care about flying,' the Blue Donkey raged. 'All I want is to teach that bird a thorough lesson.' 'But it's unworthy of you,' her friends murmured. The donkey didn't care.

The next day when the jay returned, the Blue Donkey called out cheerfully, 'I say, could you teach me to float?' 'What?' asked the jay. 'Well, flying's a bit strenuous for a beast my age; but if you could show me how to float, why then I could try it and practise in private.' 'What do you mean?' The jay was caught off-guard. 'Well, you know, floating. When you just fold your wings and sit on air.' Then the Blue Donkey looked at the jay suspiciously. 'Are you saying you don't know how to float? Perhaps I'd better ask somebody else.' 'No, no,' cried the jay. 'Of course I can float. Look, I'll show you.' And she flew into the air, folded her wings and plummeted to the ground.

The Blue Donkey cushioned her fall with a bundle of hay, but even so it was several minutes before the jay recovered. 'Did I float?' she asked. The Blue Donkey shook her head. 'Oh.' 'Would you like to float?' enquired the Blue Donkey. 'Yes.' 'Too bad,' and with that the Blue Donkey wandered off.

Afterwards the friends of the Blue Donkey reproached her. 'That episode betrays a crude morality,' they scolded. And it's at this point that they shudder involuntarily each time they repeat the tale. The truth is that the Blue Donkey had a vulgar streak. On this occasion she looked obstinate, then she glared, then she snorted. 'Tell that to the birds,' she said.

Lesson Number Three

'When I grow up,' said the Blue Donkey's niece, 'I'm going to be like you.'

'What? Patient and good and wise and gentle?'

'No. Rich and famous.'

'But I'm not rich, and as for my fame – well, it's true that my verse has received recognition . . . ' The Blue Donkey's voice trailed away. The little donkey fidgeted, but the Blue Donkey was just warming up. 'Do you want to be a poet?'

'Yes, a famous one – I mean like you,' she put in quickly before the Blue Donkey could query that.

'Little one,' the Blue Donkey spoke from the heights of experience, 'for that you'll have to practise.'

'Oh I have,' said her niece. 'I can do my autograph in five seconds flat.'

The Blue Donkey was taken aback. 'No, no, not practise being famous. I mean practise being a poet.'

'How do you do that?'

'You work night and day and you write a lot.'

'Oh.' The little donkey's face was unreadable, but she didn't say anything and the Blue Donkey did not labour the point. That was enough for the first lesson, one had to be patient.

It was some time before the Blue Donkey saw her niece again. 'Well, little one, how is the writing coming along?'

'What? Oh it's been ages since I learnt to do all that.'

The Blue Donkey decided it was now time for the second lesson. 'Just being able to read and write doesn't make a poet. A poet – '

'I know,' the niece interrupted. 'I've changed my mind.'

The Blue Donkey was most disappointed. 'I thought you wanted to be a poet like me?'

'Oh I want to be a poet.' The Blue Donkey brightened. 'But not like you.'

'I see.' The Blue Donkey paused. 'You're doing all right,'

she told her thoughtfully. Then as her niece trotted away, the Blue Donkey sighed. 'That was Lesson Number Three,' she informed herself.

A Tale of Triumph

'I had a dream,' the Blue Donkey announced to her friend, Suniti. Suniti settled back. She was in for it.

'In my dream,' the Blue Donkey continued, 'a critic told me I didn't exist.'

'Why didn't you exist?' asked Suniti dutifully.

'Well, the critic said: "Where are the men? Where are the machines? In a well-ordered world donkeys don't talk. In fact by the twentieth century they're obsolete."'

'What did you say?'

'I pointed out that he was talking to me.'

'And then what happened?'

'He gave me a lecture on literary form. He got quite excited. "The fact of your blueness is an incontrovertible clue to the nature of your being." I didn't understand what he was saying. Suddenly he became very patient. "Don't you see? You are a product of the imagination. You are a fabulous beast." "Did you imagine me?" I asked him politely. "Certainly not!" He sounded so indignant that I backed away a step or two; but I wanted to understand so I asked him again. "Well, who imagined me?" He looked me up and down. "I expect you did," he said abruptly. Then he vanished.'

'And then you woke up?'

'No, I cropped some grass and fell asleep.'

The Blue Donkey was looking at Suniti expectantly.

Suniti frowned. 'It's a Tale of Triumph,' she said at last. 'Your creative instincts vanquished the critic.'

But the Blue Donkey still looked puzzled. 'Did the critic exist?' she asked timidly.

'Oh yes. Critics are an incontrovertible fact of life.'

'But I thought I abolished him?'

'Not quite. Even in your dreams you do not behave like a homicidal beast.'

The Blue Donkey smiled. She was vastly relieved.

'Like amorous birds of prey ...'

If sweet robin singing in my throat
  were a murderous bird
                setting his songs afloat
without any care of how he troubled
                the placid air,
then crystals might form and crack and snap
and hearts pop and minstrels rap
out their tuneful melodies, and the world
that disastrous robin had shaped seem
innocent like a baby curled
up in a colourful dream
of blood, which spattered everywhere
engendered miracles of pain and despair.

But oh no, no.
                Robin is a coward,
  says that the world thus devoured
        will cause heartache and headache,
        gut rot and bellyache,
  which to do, he, poor thing, is not empowered.

Tell the bird he's a lurid liar.
  No puling poet need aspire
to curb convulsion by silent revulsion.
World will whirl in her solar fire
whether poet and robin rage or retire.

Le Bel Ange

(i)

One day an amorous angel said to me, 'Tu es une belle indienne.' 'Oh no,' I said, 'I don't speak French,' and shuffled, but felt so very, so extraordinarily happy, I smiled. 'Parmi toutes les femmes ici, je t'ai choisie,' she said. 'Oh golly,' I said, tried not to gulp, but she didn't seem to mind. 'J'aime tes bras, tes seins, tes cheveux, ton visage, ta voix, tes lèvres, ton corps, tes genoux,' she said. I felt so embarrassed I dropped my eyes. But then this angel took me in her arms. 'Que tu es belle!' I said and was reconciled.

(Q. To what was I reconciled?
A. To having my knees admired.)

(ii)

Le deuxième jour l'ange m'a dit, 'Il faut que tu changes.' 'What do you mean?' I said. 'Do you mean my clothes?' 'Pas tes vêtements,' she said. I found myself melting in the light of her glance, et j'ai changé et je change encore. Bientôt elle trouvera qu'elle est la belle femme et que je suis l'ange.

(iii)

'Les anges, qu'est-ce-qu'ils font?' lui ai-je demandé. 'Est-ce-qu'ils peinent, est-ce-qu'ils filent, est-ce-qu'ils mangent?' 'Pas du tout,' a-t-elle répondu. 'Ils aiment les belles femmes et ils chantent, ils chantent.' Alors, j'ai su que ceci était mon métier et que je ferais mes devoirs comme un ange, un bel ange.

Crow and Starling

Once upon a time there was an idiot crow. She was sensible enough most of the time, but utterly foolish when she fell in love or fancied anybody. Now, it so happened that she met a starling. The starling was charming, the crow was charmed, but she decided that for once she was going to be sensible. She was calm, dispassionate and moderately friendly. At last one day they met again. Crow had pined and repined dreadfully, but in accordance with her decision to do nothing foolish, she had done nothing. Once again Starling and Crow were very sensible and reasonably friendly. Soon they began to meet often. They continued calm, quiet and friendly. It became a habit. They got used to it. So that it was only occasionally that Crow tore her feathers and cursed her wisdom and her folly.

Cythera

Small rivulets ran about her feet
    and backwards to the ocean.
I knew who she was,
    but she walked through the waves
and sat down beside me.
        I stayed very still.
She said that it was hot.
I didn't say anything, but I thought
  to myself I would make a poem
  out of this, of how I sat on a beach
  and gossiped with a goddess, and of
  how kind she was and friendly.
Her movements were slow. 'She's lazy,'
  I decided. 'Olympians have the time
  and are therefore unhurried.'
I wondered how I looked, but she was
  combing her hair. I waited quietly.
  And then she smiled. I was
  very ashamed. She was my friend
  and I had made her a goddess:
        that shamed me.

Olive Branch

Athene and her owl were sitting among the scrub on scraggy rocks. Below them the sea was unwrinkled blue.

'They call me my father's daughter,' Athene muttered angrily.

'What's so bad about that?' responded the owl. 'They call me Athene's Owl. Once someone even tried "Minerva's Minion".' The owl shrugged. 'There's absolutely no point in getting ruffled.'

'You don't understand.'

'What don't I understand?'

'It's all a matter of identity and gender. To you it doesn't matter. You're only an owl. But the modern women are turning against me. They say that I'm really on the side of the men.'

'Well, aren't you?' enquired the owl.

'Don't be absurd. I'm a goddess, you know. I only dabble in important matters. When the men were running things, obviously I took the side of the men – against other men, it might be pointed out.'

'What about Arachne? What about Clytemnestra? Oh, and Medusa as well?' murmured the owl.

'I was dispensing justice. And justice has to do with the rules as they are, I mean, were.'

'Well there you are then.' The owl was getting bored. 'You have behaved impeccably and have absolutely nothing to worry about.'

'Oh you silly bird! Don't you understand that the times have changed and that in accordance with the times I have to change my image?'

'I'm not a silly bird,' replied the owl.

'Be helpful then.'

'What is your problem?'

'I haven't got a mother and I have no female friends.'

'Oh you silly goddess! Don't you know that it's impossible for anyone not to have a mother? Look at the olive branch you

46

hold in your hand.'

'Well, who is my mother?'

'The earth is your mother.'

'And who is my friend?'

'I am your sister and your friend.'

Athene was startled. 'All these years you never said a word . . .'

'You didn't want to know.'

'What do we do now?' For the first time in her life she felt unsure.

'Now we go into the world and meet our fellow women. For the time being, however, I'll do the talking. You stay in the background.'

And that was how it came about that the owl and her sister rejoined the world.

The Return of the Giantess

There were the usual reverberations,
                              a racket
in the sky, birds squabbling
                              and swerving and mating,
fanfare of flowers, feathers
                              falling,
that sort of thing.
                              There were
the subterranean tremors,
                              the ambiguous weather,
hot and cold spells,
                              and the unambiguous dreams.
That the return of the giantess
                              would be noiseless
and reticent was not to be expected.
                              I had had warning.
But when she came, bending the green wave
of grass before her, treading the mountains
and – though courteous as ever – trampling
                              the hills,
and I opened my arms wide,
                              and wider
to receive her, neither grass, nor sky,
nor the pounding sea could hold her in,
and I held her close and we had our fill.

'If You Know What I Mean'

Since it was the traditional thing for jackals to do, one afternoon a young jackal went to court and said to the lioness, 'O my Lady, you are terrific. You are Queen of the Beasts. You are superb. You are dazzling. Your coat is marvellous and so on, if you know what I mean.'

'I know what you mean,' replied the lioness. 'But you are tedious, little jackal. Go away and learn courtly speech.'

The jackal went away and worked hard. She listened to her elders, studied rhetoric, and when she had composed at least half a dozen compliments with which she was satisfied, she returned to the lioness and tried out the first.

'O Lady,' she ventured, 'when the sun goes down your burnished fur gives light to lesser creatures who inhabit the night.'

'Not true,' returned the lioness. 'And a nuisance if it were. How would I stalk, how hunt, whom kill?'

The jackal wanted to say that though it wasn't true, it was at least poetic, but the lioness was frowning. The jackal went away. This time she applied herself for five long years. The lioness, meanwhile, had got older and even more bad tempered.

'What do you want?' she asked crossly when the jackal reappeared.

'I want to please.'

The lioness grunted and without troubling to say anything, she went back to sleep.

The jackal sat there and watched the lioness. After a while she fetched out an instrument and began to sing. It was a long and complicated song about a sleeping lioness and a singing jackal. The lioness, of course, continued to sleep. She twitched and turned, sometimed she snored, sometimes she half woke up and blinked uneasily. At last she yawned and stretched and shook herself and woke up properly.

The jackal was still there.

'What? Are you still here?' asked the lioness. 'What do you want?'

This time the jackal just sat there with downcast eyes and very carefully did not speak.

The tired lioness glared at her. At last she said, 'Oh, all right. You can stay at court. But remember, only lullabyes, and only when I'm asleep.'

Dear Reader,

I have the power? I define? And I
control? But it takes two live bodies, one
writing and one reading, to generate a sky,
a habitable planet and a working sun.
The colour of my sun happens to be yellow.
Yours too, you say? I feel so pleased. Our task
is made easier. We are not fighters, but fellow-
travellers? – would you say? – enabled to bask
in our mutual glow. But it's there you baulk.
What would have happened, you wish to know,
if your sun had been the colour of milky chalk
or had presented a more muted show?
What can I say? Perhaps I'd have shouted, 'Yellow!
Bright yellow!' and you'd have refused to say it was so.

Loner

It so happened that a queen made friends with a deer. She had been sensible, had proceeded slowly, and in time the deer had learned to feed from her hand. When the queen entered the forest to be with the deer, she would tell the courtiers to stay far away. The king, who was uxorious, made no objection. Eventually she took to going out early in the mornings and returning in the evenings. At first the king did not notice, but one evening when she was later than usual, he asked where she had been and why she was late. 'I haven't been anywhere,' she answered mildly; 'just into the forest.' And there the matter rested, but the gossip spread. At last one evening the queen failed to return. Courtiers whispered, the palace guard was roused, the king frowned. They marched into the forest and hunted for the queen. She was nowhere to be found. The king was furious. There were rumours about that the queen had had a lover and that he, the king, looked like a fool. Every morning he would ride into the forest. Every morning the courtiers would follow. They would let fly their arrows at anything that moved. In the end the birds and beasts pleaded with the queen to return to the king. Their lives were at stake. So the queen said goodbye and returned to the palace. And there she remains, distinct from the beasts and surrounded by men.

Scylla: An Exegesis

A man-eating bitch: the term is exact,
since she ate men, crunching them horribly,
six at a time as a matter of fact,
between her teeth. But it's easy to see,
if we follow Virgil and exercise tact,
that in this there's a certain propriety.
For she had loved a man, and by him scorned,
had thrown herself into the sea,
there churned and yearned until transformed,
and thus enabled to feed to satiety.
Now so much is clear: the gods are just
and make a mockery of all our lust.
'Is' and 'ought' turn to 'seems'
as we fulfil our horrid dreams.
But there is one point which still troubles me:
what did the men she swallowed want to be?

Dazzler

The sunbird was showing off to such a degree, making the light vibrate off her wingtips, obviously and blatantly singing to herself, that the duck frowned. The sunbird ignored her; she was executing a wholly unnecessary somersault. The duck spoke: 'You ought not to racket and rocket about in quite that manner.' The sunbird was astonished. She stopped in mid-flight and reversed herself. The duck winced – more showing off. 'Why not? It's great fun. Come and try it yourself.' 'You spoil the atmosphere.' The duck was sounding more and more cross. The sunbird by now was bouncing up and down on the end of a twig. 'What, by flying in it?' Suddenly she shot high into the air. The duck felt pacified – she had driven away the nuisance, when the sunbird whizzed past. 'You're a hyperactive headache!' the duck shouted. 'Why? What do I do wrong?' The sunbird was swinging from a nearby creeper. 'You occupy space,' muttered the duck. 'Not as much as you,' retorted the sunbird. The duck lost her temper. With a great flapping of wings she rushed at the sunbird. The sunbird dodged. The duck chased her. At last when the duck was certain that the sunbird had gone, she settled down again to sun herself. Three seconds later she heard the sunbird saying, 'I told you it was fun. Now I'll chase you and you dodge.'

Question: If you were a duck, what would you do?
  (a) practise patience
  (b) move
  (c) start a campaign to make sunbirds illegal
  (d) ask the sunbird for flying lessons.

Magpie

A magpie finds a golden coin. Oh good. She picks it up neatly and takes it to her nest. There it glints and glitters in the sun. The magpie enjoys it, but a woman comes along.

'O Magpie, I see you have some money in your nest.'

'What?'

'Money!' says the woman. 'That thing that glitters. Don't you understand the value of money?'

'No,' says the magpie.

'Well, then give it to me,' cajoles the woman, 'because I do.'

'No,' says the magpie.

The woman decides to change her tactics. 'Look, if you give me that coin, I'll give you ten others to put in its place.' She means to give the bird bits of tinsel.

'No,' says the magpie.

The woman is beginning to feel exasperated. 'Oh you silly bird! Don't you understand simple arithmetic?'

'Not really,' says the magpie.

'But it isn't fair. Why should you have something you don't even understand?'

'Why not?' asks the magpie.

The woman sits down and patiently explains justice and money and simple arithmetic. At last she stops. She glares at the bird. 'Now will you give me the golden coin?'

'No,' says the magpie.

'What! Didn't you understand everything I said?'

'Yes, I did,' says the magpie.

'What did you understand?'

'That money glitters. That ten is equal to one sometimes, and sometimes it isn't. And that justice, as you said, is strictly for the birds.'

Then she picks up the coin in her strong beak and flies off somewhere where it's more quiet.

If somehow I might . . .

If somehow I might have the vision
to see humans in their simple reversion
to animals, neither bitter, brutal, nor conscious
of being anything other than themselves, ungracious
in nothing, and unaware of the need
to present a flattering picture of their greed,
then perhaps some strutting and well-nourished male
might seem merely a beautiful animal
in all the splendour of his rutting season,
and I, having no reason to fear distress,
might find occasion to feel blessed and bless.

The Bride

Once upon a time there was a proud young prince, and he had reason to be proud. He was heir to the kingdom, he was handsome and healthy, he had been extremely well educated, and all the social graces that could reasonably be taught had been carefully inculcated. What was more, his father was a king, and his father's father, and his father before that, so that his right to rule was undisputed. Now, when it was time for this young man to marry, he said to his father, 'Father, you have always said that only the best was fit for me. I have the best falcons, and the best hounds and the best stallions in all the world. But where will you find a bride who is worthy of me?' The king didn't think that this would be much of a problem. He had contests instituted throughout the kingdom. There were contests for beauty, and contests for strength, and contests for knowledge and intelligence and wit, and there were skill-testing contests for all sorts of things such as archery and music. When the tests were done, the winners of the contests were presented to the prince. He looked them over. Their credentials were good. Indeed, he began to be afraid that some of their credentials were better than his. 'These women have excelled,' he said to his father, 'but they seem to be lacking in the womanly qualities.' 'Well, of course,' said his father. 'I have weeded these out. You can now choose from those who did not compete.'

Baffled Beast

Said the fox to herself, having examined the bright and glossy grapes, 'It's true they're out of reach, and it's equally true I desire them avidly. What have we here? Not a contradiction in terms, but two solitary truths rolling like marbles on the top of my mind.' This image quite pleased her, she smiled complacently: 'What a nice mind!' She basked in the sun, she whiled away time, till a glint from the grapes sent the Idea of the Grape careering so wildly at its twin truth that poor fox had to hang on to her head and shut her eyes tight.

Look, Medusa!

Medusa living on a remote shore
troubled no one: fish swam, birds flew, and the sea
did not turn to glass. All was as before.
A few broken statues lay untidily
on the lonely beach, but other than these
there was nothing wrong with that peaceful scene.
And so, when the hero Perseus came to seize
the Gorgon's head, he thought he might have been
mistaken. He watched for a while, but she turned
nothing to stone. The waves roared as waves will,
till at last the hidden hero burned
to be seen by her whom he had come to kill.
'Look, Medusa, I am Perseus!' he cried,
thus gaining recognition before he died.

Birds of a Feather

A magpie and a robin at the edge of a well compare reflections.

'Brighter than you.' Thus chirpy Robin.

'Bigger, better and more dapper than you.' Magpie scowling and shoving a little, puffing himself up.

'Yeah, but that snowy shirt front – inclined to get a bit dingy in the end.' Robin protesting, fluffing up feathers, beady eyes rolling to trace the curvature of his own red front.

A peck and a squawk, a wicked glitter: they're about to fight, when a wren comes up.

'Both dowdy and dingy.' Magpie and Robin glance at each other. 'The female of a species . . . ' They shake their heads. They look tolerant. Then they preen and smirk, and feel greatly cheered up.

On that island . . .

On that island where all the men turned into pigs
– there was no exception, the hero dreamt –
I stood there watching the local antics
and I found myself enjoying them.
The brilliant sun was bouncing off each porcelain back
and they looked so pink, so pretty, so piglike
with their snouts and trotters in lacquered black
that I confess I was charmed, forgot my dislike
of men behaving like pigs, and of women
who catered to them. So I said to Circe,
'They delight and dazzle. But what next? What then?
Is it all a matter of sheer artistry?
Of prancing in a patterned tapestry?
Are they pleasure-giving pigs or ordinary men?'
'Oh well,' she smiled. 'They serve a function.
                                        Piglets must please.
But tomorrow, if you like, we'll try another species.'

Playboy

Because the mermaids were surging and sighing,
baring their bosoms above the sea,
I thought that all this expressive commotion
was intended solely to pleasure me.

But it was not so, and could not have been so;
they did such things that I blushed to see,
yet seemed so oblivious of my presence there,
I knew they were merely baiting me.

I paused for a moment, then flung off my clothes,
descended upon them impetuously.
I battered the waves, I scattered the foam,
was spurned and overturned by that careless sea.

And the maids meanwhile, growling and groaning,
snarling and laughing, each glorious body
stinking of fish, displayed themselves, unaware
of my rage, undisturbed in their ecstasy.

Subsurface Sonics

Two women sat on the shore, wishing to understand the sea's sound. One of them jotted down musical notes. 'Its basic beat is three/four time.' The other fiddled with the tapes she had made. 'Perhaps,' she said, 'but no wistful waltz, no easy rhyme.' 'Mermaids . . . ' the first murmured at last. She bent her head, she sighed. The other frowned in quiet disapproval. 'Your romantic notions may distort its voice.' But the first stretched out on the sands and groaned, 'I am trying to imitate its baffled beat, its ceaseless cries.' The other merely looked at the sea, its tilting planes, its curved inclines, till she on the sands jumped to her feet. 'Well, let's go. I think I understand the sea's noise.' 'Yes?' asked the other rising slowly. 'It's polite and placid and a waste of time.'

It's not that the landscape...

Birds and Pine Tree, style of Kano Motonobu (1426–1559)
(Eugene Fuller Memorial Collection)

It's not that the landscape is colourless,
though, the fact is, it's barely dawn.
It's just the birds, their fragile happiness,
their unconscious tenderness, which they shed on
everything, till bird and tree and light are one.
Oh neither you nor I could enter there.
We'd tread on the grass, we'd switch on the sun
and baffle the landscape with our mere
humanity. We would cast long shadows,
discolour the world we had come upon.
But we can watch the birds: who comes, who goes,
how their shared delight pleases everyone,
and how, being ignorant birds and unaware,
they live at ease in their native air.

A Love Story

One day, as you walked outdoors, you found a stone. At first you thought that it might be a toad; but it was not warm, it was not slimy, and it did not quiver as you held it in your hand. You left it in your pocket. It occupied space. It had mass. But it was not an abrasive or obtrusive stone. You were not troubled; and the stone, in turn, was probably content. When you came home that night and undressed for bed, you took the stone out and set it on the dresser. It is possible, of course, that the stone watched you all night long. But then it must be remembered that the stone had no eyes. It is much more likely that it merely sat. It was contiguous in space. It was, if you like, a contemporary of yours. The following morning you lost the stone. You may have noticed its absence in your pocket. The stone may have sensed the increased distance from a source of warmth. But that was all. It is not conceivable that anything else could possibly have been felt. I conjecture, of course. The tale is, after all, a fanciful invention, a playful variation, on a species of love.

Weed

Let's take an axe, my darling, and hack
at this weed, which even now flourishes so
it would seem all our neglect and lack
of care served only to make it grow.
We did not plant it. No, neither you nor I
need admit to such a thing. We both know
how on several occasions we willed it to die,
and, believing it dead, we let it grow.
It's already a sapling. Once we're dead
and lie helplessly in the earth below,
it will wave its triumphant green overhead,
and the passing stranger will not know
that this tree whose force is still unspent
survives and thrives in spite of us, and not by intent.

Lady Tig

In the end they all said, all right, feminists had a point and it was only fair that the lady be given a similar choice. So they locked up the hero and they locked up the tiger in an adjoining cell. They covered up the cells, blindfolded the lady and informed her briefly of the nature of the choice. Now the lady wasn't silly. She knew perfectly well which was which and even more clearly what was what. The jailers betrayed it by the nature of their jokes, by the lewd look which shone in their eyes. There wasn't much choice. 'I give up,' said the lady. 'But it's the tiger's turn now. Give the tiger a choice.' So they brought out the tiger and explained carefully that though the man was larger, the flesh of the lady was more greatly prized, but it was up to the tiger; let the tiger decide. 'Right,' said the tiger and killed once, then killed again, and again and again, displaying, as it were, a natural justice, but even so, the surviving jailers seemed dissatisfied.

Poem for a Grey Day

If a parakeet chattered in a yellow sun,
if a fool snickered and a bird replied,
what's it to me? When the fable is done
the pale, cold snow still stains the mountainside.

But if the bird were bronze and metallic enough,
if its movements were powered by an atomic pile,
if it had stainless insides, was cruel and tough,
would it not serve? At least for a while?

That sun never blazed – if it did, it was so
long ago mere memory falters now –
and in a cold country its pale white shadow
illuminating as it does a paler show

only makes clear: what was lost, was lost outright.
And yet, the artificial bird in its natural rage
could ignite, if it chose, a candid page,
and stand there, an exotic alien burning bright.

Craft

There was once a poet who, aware that her reputation had reached a certain point and was climbing sluggishly, decided that in the interests of more rapid progress, a boost was needed. She committed suicide. Then surfaced once again in another country in a different disguise. At first she thought her success partial. Her reputation climbed by only a few points. But within a year it had reached the desirable upper heights. There was a call out now for her early work, the misplaced manuscripts, undestroyed letters, chance remarks and apocryphal anecdotes. She was in business again and spent the rest of her life supplying the industry. A wasted life? If asked, she'd have disagreed. She was merely engaged in doing profitably what she had always done: making up myths, creating, as it were, a suitable self, fabricating, as you've heard, the necessary lies.

Among Tigers

Must live among tigers, but can take time off
when the tigers are busy or have fed enough
to admire their prowess, their muscular grace,
the easy assurance of a lordly race.
From their point of view I exist, of course,
but am hardly central, a fact of sorts,
and of no consequence to their magnificence . . .

To bait a tiger – a fearful boast:
but given their 'norms', their manners and laws
such a deed would elicit no applause.
And yet, it might be worth it – almost –
to observe in action a tiger's reaction.

You see, I have survived so long,
my habit of observation grown so strong
that sometimes I think I almost belong.
I know exactly how a tiger drinks,
how a tiger walks, smiles and thinks,
but find somehow that I cannot ape
that unthinking pride or its manifest shape.
I fully understand the Tigrish Cause
and keep my distance from those massive jaws.

What the One-eyed Monkey Said to the Tigers
or
Friends and Fellow Aliens

When so many have died so senselessly
does it matter that I myself should prove
an exception? And that at my going,
or refusal to go, the world should await
with uplifted pencils and gaping microphones
some final, factual, definitive act?
No, not the dying or death's postponement,
but the meaning of the thing, some loud word,
so that the audience, relieved, leans back
thinking, 'It remains only that now we clap.'
A trivial deception and not uncommon.
Better perhaps to go a little mad,
to buttonhole strangers and whisper horridly,
'All my life I have silently hated you,
but since you're going to die, I am willing
to dislike you a little less for that.'

71

Gracious Living

The one-eyed monkey had been invited to tea by the rabbits. She didn't know the rabbits well and was uncertain about protocol. Should she take flowers, and should they be edible? She pondered these questions as she made her way towards the farmyard. When she came to the well, she gathered marigolds. Marigolds would do, marigolds couldn't possibly offend. Then she leaned over and examined her reflection. She looked neat and tidy – even handsome, she thought. When she turned away she found a number of hens staring at her. 'What are you doing?' they wanted to know.

Now the one-eyed monkey knew perfectly well that the rabbits and hens didn't get on; she said, 'Oh, I was just making sure I looked all right.'

The hens were persistent. 'Why?' they enquired.

'I'm going to have tea with the rabbits.' She had half expected trouble, but the hens just turned away and said nothing more.

She arrived at the rabbit hutch. It looked airy and comfortable. One of the rabbits let her in and they all greeted her, 'Welcome, Sister.' The one-eyed monkey was taken aback. Sister? But she didn't want to be rude; she muttered, 'Welcome.' Then she realised it was the wrong response; luckily the rabbits seemed oblivious.

She nibbled a leaf. Conversation, she discovered, was not going to be difficult. The rabbits talked among themselves, and every now and then – when it was possible – she put in a word. Out of the corner of her eye she noticed that the hens had returned to the yard. Soon they were clucking furiously around the hutch, but the rabbits' chatter did not diminish. They were undisturbed. The one-eyed monkey said nothing, but she remembered that the ownership of the hutch had been controversial. She turned to the rabbits. The eldest was addressing her. 'We invited you to tea to ask you to join our organisation. All fellow creatures have certain problems in common.'

The one-eyed monkey didn't know what to say. She hated organisations; they involved meetings and committees and long discussions. 'Ah, oh, well,' she began when one of the problems the rabbits had referred to manifested itself.

'Quick! Run! Hide!' shrieked the rabbits. 'Why?' asked the monkey, but before she knew it she had been bundled under a pile of leaves and four or five rabbits were sitting on her. After a while the commotion died down, and she felt the rabbits removing the leaves. The one-eyed monkey crawled out and stood there among the rabbits. A tired marigold drooped from one ear. She was furious. 'What was all that about?'

'That was the farmer. The farmer shoots monkeys,' responded a young rabbit.

'Yes,' put in an elderly rabbit. 'If the humans had caught us consorting with monkeys, heaven knows what would have happened. They'd have thrown us out.'

'And the hens would have taken over.'

'We couldn't let the farmer see you, you know,' added an intellectual rabbit. 'You see, the really important thing is that the farmer mustn't find out that we can unlock the hutch.'

The one-eyed monkey glared at them. 'The really important thing,' she told them briefly, 'is that you haven't found out what you can do once you have unlocked the hutch.' Then she walked out.

The door hung open. Behind her back a few of the hens made a concerted rush for the gaping entrance.

The hermit in her wisdom ...

The hermit in her wisdom was casting stones
at the birds in the breeze. 'Come to pick my bones,'
she chortled, 'but not yet, and not until
the desert air has given me my fill
of life and breath and ceaseless meditation
and my mind, fixed in strong and steady contemplation,
at last, circles to a stop, and is still.'
But birds also have a purpose to fulfil.
They wheeled and shrieked, 'You cause us vexation
and needless despair. We must whirl in agitation
until, dear hermit, you learn to sit still.'
Then the hermit sat down and relaxed her will;
her fists unclenched, one by one she dropped the stones,
while the hungry birds settled down to dine at once.

The Fortunate One

Once upon a time the gods decided to be lavish in their blessings. 'We will make you a queen,' they told the little girl. 'Thank you,' she said, a bit startled, but not really knowing what else to say. She supposed that being a queen was probably a good thing. 'And we will give you a king who is a genuinely good person, and who will help you with everything.' She said, 'Thank you,' again. A helpful partner was almost certainly a good thing; being a queen might be difficult and she could do with some help. 'And we will give you five children who will prosper reasonably and seventeen grandchildren to go with them.' The little girl looked doubtful. Seventeen grandchildren was rather a lot; but she decided that on the whole they'd turn out to be nice.

'Have we left out anything?' The gods murmured among themselves. 'Oh yes, you will have excellent health and a long life – and you will also be intelligent and beautiful.' This last was an afterthought. The little girl shuffled her feet, thinking she was being dismissed at last; but the gods weren't done with her. 'There's one more thing,' they informed the child. 'For all these gifts we hold you responsible. Do you agree?' For the first time the little girl felt apprehensive: what did it mean to be held responsible? But since there wasn't very much she could say to the gods, she said, 'Yes.'

Well, everything turned out as they had said it would. And when her long life came to an end, she knew she would have to face the gods. So she prepared an apologetic speech in advance. The gods summoned her. She dared not look at them. She launched into her speech. 'I tried to be a responsible queen, but in time somehow the kingdom dissolved. And even the money trickled away. As for the children, they are all right, but not as prosperous as I once was. Both beauty and good health, and even my power over words, faded at the last. And now of my long life nothing is left. I could not preserve any of your gifts. I ask your pardon.' She was certain that the gods were displeased with her.

But the gods merely said, 'So you think you were a failure?'

'Yes,' she answered humbly. 'You gave me wealth and power, and I lost it all.'

'And you thought we expected you to keep it forever? Had you power over time?'

'No,' she faltered.

'You were only expected to try to grow to your full stature. And from that responsibility as a queen or a mother or an ordinary woman you didn't abdicate. Come, do you still think you failed utterly?'

'No,' she ventured, 'but I failed often . . .'

At that the gods laughed. 'But you weren't a god,' they remarked, 'only a queen.'

So she looked up at last and smiled at them.

Eurydice

Death was rather sudden, but pleasant enough.
He came. I rose, gliding smoothly through
the green wood. The going was easy, not rough;
I had no hesitation about what to do.
Death made it simple: he led, I followed.
There was no question, he knew that I would.
And I didn't mind at all that he chose the road;
I was his forever, that was understood.
And so, when my lover came, brave and confident,
and won me from Death by means of his charm,
what could I do, but prove obedient?
He led. I followed till some slight alarm
made him look back, and then I fled, since he
was not Death's master, but a slave, like me.

Ivory Apes

The one-eyed monkey was touting a petition. It was reasonable enough, merely asking that one-eyed monkeys, or indeed monkeys of any other kind, not be shot at for the sole purpose of sport or pleasure. But she needed signatures, so she wrote to her cousins, the No Sisters, asking if she might drop in for a chat with them. The three cousins all lived together in a large tree, and each one of them had contrived a method, peculiar to herself, for coping with the world. When the letter arrived, the First Cousin declared she was unable to read it. The Second Cousin said that she herself could read it all right, but was prohibited by her rule from replying to it. The Third Cousin permitted herself both to read and write. She answered the letter: the one-eyed monkey was most welcome, but for obvious reasons she herself could not participate in any discussion.

The one-eyed monkey was a little put out by this odd behaviour, but she was also curious. On the appointed day she presented herself at the foot of their tree. She could see her three cousins perched on a branch, but only one of them acknowledged her presence. 'Hello,' shouted the one-eyed monkey, 'would you care to read and sign this petition?' But the one who had waved seemed unable to hear her. The one-eyed monkey was very perplexed, and then she understood. Her three cousins were following the example of their illustrious ancestors, therefore their name, the No Sisters. They could see, hear and speak no evil.

'But this isn't evil,' the one-eyed monkey called out to them. She scrambled into the branches and showed them the petition. 'This is good.'

Her cousins peered at the text in front of them. At last one of them said, 'But it may cause trouble.' The second murmured, 'We want no involvement.' And the third sighed, 'Besides, how can we know what is genuinely good and what is truly evil?'

Just then a farmer appeared with a double-barrelled shot-gun. 'Look out!' cried the one-eyed monkey and hid herself, but her cousins stayed where they were.

'The farmer with the shotgun does not exist,' pronounced one monkey.

'Oh yes, I do,' the farmer replied and shot her.

'The sound of the shotgun was only an illusion. If there was a sound, it was distant thunder,' the second monkey stated.

'Oh no, it wasn't,' the farmer replied and shot her as well.

The farmer waited for the third monkey to make a remark, but since she said nothing the farmer went away. Then the two monkeys who had fallen to the ground dusted themselves, jumped into the tree and sat down again beside their sister.

The one-eyed monkey had been watching all this in terror and consternation. At last she approached them and asked diffidently, 'Please? What happened?' But the three sisters were taking no chances. They had turned into statues. Their heads were averted, their ears covered up and their eyes were shut.

The beasts came up to me . . .

The beasts came up to me and licked my hand.
I was glad of the air, glad of the moss
and its luxurious softness, and at a loss
to know why I was accepted in that land
of slow time and amiable beasts. I had done
nothing to find myself there. I had connived
with myself in the usual way, contrived
to cut losses, been glad when I won.
Surely this golden world was not for me.
It was too placid, too simple, too easy.
Any moment now the fabric would tear;
someone would say I had no business there.
And I would get up and either fight or run
while the friendly beasts looked quietly on.

Doubled and Redoubled

One day a magpie decided that the Blue Donkey was in danger of thinking too well of herself and that it was up to her, the magpie, to remedy that. Accordingly, she scuffed her feathers, muddied her breast and, swooping down on the Blue Donkey in an unsteady wobble, fell at her feet with a small thud. 'Please,' said the Blue Donkey, quite alarmed. 'What is the matter? Can I help you?' The magpie opened her eyes. 'No,' she sighed. 'I think I have died and gone to heaven.' 'Oh no,' the Blue Donkey told her. 'This isn't heaven. This is earth.' 'But in that case, are you real?' 'Yes, of course. Why not?' 'But everyone said that you were a legend.' 'Well, I'm not.' 'Oh but you are!' By now the magpie was sitting up. 'You are a saint. Where I come from just your name accomplishes miracles.' In spite of herself the Blue Donkey felt flattered. 'What sort of miracles?' she asked casually. 'Oh, problems solved, wishes granted, straw into gold, the usual thing. But I must fly away now and spread the good news that you exist and that I have met you in person.' 'No, wait,' called the Blue Donkey, but the magpie had disappeared. The Blue Donkey felt uneasy, but still, it was nice to be told that just one's name . . . She dozed off and forgot the incident.

When she woke up, she found five rabbits, two blackbirds, the magpie herself and a number of other creatures standing around, obviously waiting for something to happen.

'Hello,' said the Blue Donkey. 'Anything I can do?'

'Yes,' a rabbit spoke up. 'We've come for the miracle.'

'The miracle?'

'Yes. The magpie told us that you said you were a saint and that you could turn straw into gold.'

'I see.' The Blue Donkey thought for a moment. She looked puzzled. 'But didn't the magpie tell you that in return for her faith, I transferred half of my gift to her?'

Everybody now looked at the magpie.

'What do you mean?' The magpie was startled.

'Why it's you who can turn straw into gold.' Then the Blue Donkey added for the benefit of the others, 'It was only this morning that I saw her do it.'

'Was that a miracle? ' a blackbird enquired, wanting to be sure.

'Yes,' replied the magpie firmly. She had recovered herself. She turned to the Blue Donkey. 'But where is the gold?' she asked politely.

'Being a saintly donkey, I changed it back into straw again. There it is.' She pointed to the straw on which the blackbird was perched.

'And that, of course, was the second miracle,' the blackbird murmured, pleased that she had got the hang of the matter. She gathered up her notes. Soon the spectators had drifted away. The donkey and the magpie faced one another.

'Well, that's done,' said the Blue Donkey cheerfully.

The magpie gaped. She had expected the donkey to be furious with her. 'But aren't you cross?' she asked at last.

'Oh, I don't know. Two miracles in the course of a day, two saints where at first there were none – we did rather well.' She winked at the magpie in a friendly fashion.

The magpie couldn't understand it. 'Are you – are you really a saint?' she asked hesitantly.

'Of course not.'

'Then why aren't you angry?'

'Because,' replied the Blue Donkey, smiling broadly, 'I won.'

Serious Danger

'I had a dream the other day,' Suniti said. The Blue Donkey sighed, but fair was fair. Suniti had listened to her dream.

'In this dream,' Suniti went on, 'I was given a choice between a tiger skin and a donkey skin.'

'Why?'

'Because I'd been complaining about what it felt like to be in my own skin. Anyhow, I chose the tiger skin.'

'Indeed,' murmured the Blue Donkey.

'It was so beautiful,' Suniti explained apologetically. 'I thought I would try it. Once I'd put it on, I looked exactly like a tiger. I felt quite grand. I strolled this way and that way, but I eventually discovered that all my old friends were avoiding me now.'

'What did you do?'

'I joined the tigers.' The Blue Donkey frowned, but Suniti seemed oblivious. 'At first it was all right, but I found that they had certain tigrish customs I didn't understand.'

'What sort of customs?' asked the Blue Donkey curiously.

Suniti hesitated. 'Well, mostly to do with the sharpening of claws and killing for oneself.' She sounded embarrassed. The Blue Donkey didn't say anything. Suniti hurried on, 'Anyhow, I divested myself of the tiger skin and put on the donkey skin.'

'Sensible woman!'

'Now I looked exactly like a donkey. But there was a problem. I was allergic to grass.'

'Rubbish!' cried the Blue Donkey. 'You only thought you were.'

'Oh no,' protested Suniti. 'It was real enough. There I was, in serious danger of starving to death; and since I had lost my own skin, my only alternative was the skin of the tiger.'

'What did you do?'

'What could I do? It was a terrible choice.'

'Even so, I hope you made a moral decision.' The Blue Donkey sounded unusually severe.

Suddenly Suniti grinned at her friend. 'It's all right,' she said. 'In my dream I acquired a taste for spinach instead.'

But the Blue Donkey didn't smile back. She looked thoughtful. 'Tell me,' she said, 'is it really possible that you disliked spinach?'

Transit Gloria

'Let's face it,' the zoologist remarked, 'the donkey is not a heroic beast.'

'That isn't true,' protested the Blue Donkey.

'You mean it isn't palatable. But what does it matter? Heroism isn't everything.'

'No, I mean it isn't true. There have been dozens of distinguished donkeys.

'Name one.'

'Shanti.'

'Who?'

'Shanti, my grandmother.'

'Never heard of her.'

'That just shows you don't know what you're talking about.'

'All right,' returned the zoologist. 'Let's talk about Shanti. In how many battles did she engage and how much territory did she conquer?'

'What?' asked the Blue Donkey.

'Let's try again. Was she big and brawny and extremely powerful?'

'No,' replied the Blue Donkey. 'No, she was an ordinary size, but appearances don't matter.'

'Very well,' continued the zoologist. 'Could she bray loudly? Did she win arguments?'

'Her voice was gentle, soft and low,' murmured the Blue Donkey, beginning to feel she was losing ground.

'Well, was she a sex symbol?'

'A what?'

'Never mind.' The zoologist shrugged. 'Look, she wasn't a general, she wasn't a politician, she wasn't a star. What exactly was her claim to fame?'

'She was intelligent,' said the Blue Donkey.

'What?'

'In–tel–li–gent.'

'There you are.' The zoologist looked extremely pleased. 'Would you agree that donkeys on the whole do not argue, do not fight and do not dazzle?'

'Well, no, they don't.' The Blue Donkey paused. 'It isn't sensible.'

'Precisely.' The zoologist was beaming now. 'I have studied donkeys, and that is how donkeys think. Now, at last, do you take my point?'

'Yes,' muttered the Blue Donkey gloomily. 'In order to win I have to be stupid.'

In the Garden

The Blue Donkey and the White Unicorn were feeding on lilies. The Blue Donkey was feeling awkward. It had taken her weeks to summon the courage to ask for an interview. The unicorn had seemed a little surprised, but had agreed without difficulty; and so there was really no reason for feeling tongue-tied, the Blue Donkey told herself fiercely. Here she was in the unicorn's presence and ought to be making pleasant conversation.

'It must be wonderful to be a unicorn,' the Blue Donkey said and could have kicked herself.

But the unicorn replied amiably enough. 'It's all right. Oh look, a new variety of roses! Do let's try them. They look delicious.'

The truth was that the Blue Donkey didn't care for lilies and could only barely stomach rose petals. She did her best, and tried to comment on the taste and texture of the new rosebush. The White Unicorn nodded happily with her mouth full. For so delicate a creature she had an enormous appetite, but, of course, the Blue Donkey knew that it would be most improper to comment on that. She thought hard.

'When do you compose?'

'Compose?' asked the unicorn.

'Yes. I mean when do you do your best work? It must be at dawn. You are a creature of the dawn.' The Blue Donkey heard herself gushing and wished she hadn't.

'Oh, I don't work,' the unicorn replied.

The Blue Donkey stored away the answer. What did it mean? That the work of the true poet was unlaboured? But now that they were on the right subject, she must quickly get in another question.

'What sort of poetry do you like best?' It was feeble, but perhaps it would do.

'Poetry?' asked the White Unicorn wonderingly. 'So much of it is so mushy these days. Haven't tried any lately. Hard to digest. But it's better than novels – usually comes in smaller chunks.'

There were no roses left and only one stunted lily. Lunch was definitely over.

'Well, it was nice to meet you,' said the unicorn graciously and sauntered away.

'Goodbye,' called out the Blue Donkey, 'and thank you so much.' She stood stock still in the middle of the débris and tried to put her thoughts in order. 'Organic,' she murmured. 'That's the key word.' She stared hard at the lily. 'I – I think,' she confided, 'I think I've been vouchsafed a revelation.'

Stilted Poem

Murmur of grass, pleasure's pinpricks,
         amorous intent made explicit –
to dwell on that – what it was like –
                    that is not difficult –
indeed, it is easy.
              Or to profer the studied
and stilted compliment – that your eyes
                    were like mirrors –
that they changed – swirled –
                    were a dream
of drowning – I know that,
                        and you
have been told it. At times,
                    such things
please. But the rest?
                    Is stilted.
Stutters and stops. Then spills
                    into life,
and like life, is not finished

The Purposeless Pandas

The purposeless pandas were being televised.

'Emblematic,' they were told. 'You are emblematic and now symbolise what man has done to man, not to speak of the other species.'

'Thank you,' murmured the pandas. They were polite creatures, modest, shy, self-effacing. They were also uncertain about what 'emblematic' meant, but they understood that it was a great honour and that they would be expected to live up to it.

'We want to help you,' their friends whispered, 'and in order to do that we've persuaded people that they wish to purge themselves of decades of guilt – that's why the cameras and the press release. You are now officially an endangered species.'

'Thank you,' said the pandas, not quite sure what 'purge' meant, nor what 'help' entailed exactly; but when the friends of friends looked gratified, they felt relieved.

'Now,' said the producer. 'First things first. Here are six hundred cans of processed protein. Please taste it.'

The pandas obligingly tasted the stuff and quickly proceeded to bury it.

'What are you doing? Don't you like it?' The producer was horrified. 'It was prepared especially for penurious pandas. You must eat it.'

The pandas thought quickly. 'Well, you see,' they said, 'we were storing it away for a season of scarcity.'

The friends of friends laughed happily. 'Oh that's all right,' they told the pandas. 'There's plenty more where that comes from. We've set up factories ...'

'Next things next,' the producer went on. 'Here is your enclosure. We've fenced it about. Inside these limits you're perfectly safe. And look, we've even stuck in a few palm trees.'

'We don't eat coconuts,' a young panda muttered; but since she muttered softly nobody heard her, which, perhaps, was as it should be.

'Good. Good.' The producer was looking pleased. 'Now, smile please.'

'What?' asked the pandas.

'Smile, you sweet creatures,' the producer cajoled. 'We need the pictures for publicity.'

The pandas smiled anxiously.

'Good. Good. Now some action shots. Run about and play happily.

Even the good nature of the pandas was wearing thin. 'Please,' they protested. 'It's mid-afternoon. It's much too hot for anything.'

The friends of friends looked disappointed. They consulted among themselves and with the producer, then they smiled smoothly. 'Sure,' they said. 'Sure. All right. What we really need is a few close-ups of pandas mating. Now get a good rest. We'll be back tomorrow morning.'

They left, but the pandas' friends stayed behind. Now, nothing has been proven. The friends claim that all they did was feed the pandas on bamboo shoots and apologise. None the less, the fact remains that that night the pandas vanished. They left a note; it said: 'We are no longer endangered. Please consider us quite extinct.' A world alert was sent out at once, but all to no avail. As a result their emblematic status remains doubtful, particularly in view of the rumour that they're neither endangered, nor extinct, they are merely lurking.

Ordinary Women

I had got it all wrong –
                              about who
was supposed to rescue whom,
                              who was to judge,
who to watch, and which one of us
            was expected to set the world aright.
'Puzzling,' I thought. I looked
                    at the leaves, the trees.
I imagined the creatures hidden
                        in the leaves.
I would rather be a plant.
                        But those who were tall
we turned into knights. Those who were womanly –
                              that was obvious enough.
And those who were kingly we made
                        into kings; though the armour
didn't fit, and some women said
            they didn't know what a lady was.
'But that's okay,' everybody said.
                        'We'll redesign, readjust.'
I was a knight –
            I was courteous, I was tough, but not
                  tall enough. I sat among the women
                              and watched the knights.
I lounged among the knights and watched
                              the women. At last
somebody said, 'This really won't do.'
                        So we all got up.
We mixed and we mingled, we shared
                        a common cause.
Halfway through it all I fell in love.
        'There is no wooer and no one is wooed,'
                        my lady informed me.
'Fine,' I replied and looked expectant.

'And you are not a knight.'
'No,' I agreed. She nodded approval.
'And what this means
is that you and I are equals in love.'
'Yes,' I said smiling happily,
'we love one another like two ordinary women.'
But she quickly demurred,
'I was always a lady – '
And at last I understood.
'Right,' I said. 'You are a lady, and I
am a lesbian.'

Pandas Lurking

But these pandas who were lurking – what did they live on, how subsist? This question puzzled everyone. Some scholars argued that pandas required nothing at all in the way of subsistence, the fact that they had so subsisted was proof of this. Pandas, they said, were not worth discussing.

However, their opponents maintained that there was a distinct possibility that PANDAS WERE EVERYWHERE, and that occasional reports from all over the globe of pandas suddenly exposing themselves and then vanishing ought to be taken very seriously. Their point was that anyone at all, absolutely anyone, could be and probably was *a panda in disguise*. Their followers took to wearing badges which stated clearly: I AM NOT A PANDA IN DISGUISE.

All this created certain problems, which the authorities insist are being dealt with. Those who do not wear the badges are now regarded as PANDAS DISGUISED. By the removal of a badge an individual can, of course, switch categories – legislative measures are pending. But the real question now which troubles everyone is that, after all this time, should an honest-to-goodness panda reappear, her fur burnished, her eyes glowing, her nose twitching, would she be recognised?

When my love lay sleeping...

When my love lay sleeping,
                    it was not I,
it was the sun who splashed her
with sticky honey.
                        The sun
put it there. I merely watched,
patiently.
                    And it was the air,
mistaking her breasts
                        for gentle hills,
or, not mistaking at all,
                        but finding
a landscape so pleasing and rare,
                        who caressed her,
sleeping.
                    And it was the grass.
Its flickering tongues licked
                    at her feet,
crept up her thighs
                        and played
with her hair.
                    Oh it was the lascivious grass
that made my love sigh
                        and show herself
to me.

Triptych

(i)

A placid cow was grazing in the meadows. She wasn't really thinking about anything, except perhaps about the texture of the grass, its springy resilience, about a patch of clover, about the taste of buttercups, about flies, and the warmth of the sun beating on her back. In other words she was simply grazing. When suddenly a half-grown lion cub bounded from the woods. It was a ball of sunshine, a bundle of joy. It danced up to the cow and licked her all over with its rough tongue. It was importunate. It was friendly. It insisted that the cow play with it. And the cow, poor beast, was so exceedingly flattered, she soon complied, to the end that you see: a penitent cow, and an astounded lion cub begging piteously for a piece of beef.

The point of the tale? It depends rather on which of the two you identify with.

(ii)

And yet the cow we are speaking of was a Brahmini cow, had the long slender legs of Indian cattle, the quiet eyes, wistful and expressive, the curving horns, the elegant dewlap, and that masterly sweep from shoulder to rump which seems to say this is the way cattle should be made, this and only this. And she was skinny – all the better to admire her bones, their indisputable integrity. What is more, though not tended and praised as a goddess ought to be, she was used to some lip-service. This she accepted gently and calmly, never once altering her docile expression; and when chased out of gardens with sticks and stones, it is true that she ran, but she ran with a slow and clumsy dignity. So much for this beast. And what of the cub? The golden lion cub whose genes proclaimed a royal heredity? They played together, these incongruous two, the burnished cub against her white flanks making them look like a scene from heraldry. Oh they were beautiful. They were gleaming. They recalled the world before the fall. They were like milk and honey.

(iii)

Conversely Moon-Calf in love with the Lady Lioness: 'O Queen of the Jungle, Princess of Night, allow me, if you will, to entertain you with my grief.' Lioness a little anxious, has other things to do, but Moon-Calf distracting and rather dazzling in the light of moonbeams. Speaks to the Moon-Calf: 'Go away, Moon-Calf. Come back again in another five years. Then we shall see.' Five years elapse. Moon-Cow returns. Lioness and Moon-Cow become excellent friends, lovers as well, pick pretty patterns in the smooth moonbeams.

To Be a Poet

Saying that this was what it felt like to put
the right foot forward, and then the left, saying
that this was the taste of morning porridge,
that of milk, and this other of a niggling
but persistent pain, saying –
that, I suppose, was what was distinctive –
being unable to keep my mouth shut,
my mind from working. But a poet lives
like any other creature, talks perhaps
more than is normal, her doom no brighter,
nor her death less dismal than any other.

From the Apocrypha

They had set up the Blue Donkey as the pythoness. She had told them that this was absurd, that a four-legged donkey could not balance with any degree of dignity on a three-legged stool; and they had said, well, all right, they'd dispense with the stool. She had then stipulated that the seekers after truth only be admitted one at a time and they had said that that was all right too provided they could videotape the entire session. The Blue Donkey had then sat down and refused to move. As a result a small crowd had gathered about. They were waiting to see what she would do. But the Blue Donkey did absolutely nothing. She twitched her right ear, then her left and then she nosed her way through the crowd. 'That'll teach them,' she muttered to herself, and, of course, it did. The following day when the cult gathered, they took as their text, 'Look neither to the left, nor to the right, but follow your nose,' and as a sub-text, 'Keep all four feet firmly on the ground.'

Stumbling Block

'Oh! I'm sorry!' cried the Blue Donkey and jumped backwards.

'Watch where you're going,' growled the caterpillar. 'You nearly stepped on me.'

'I said I was sorry,' mumbled the Blue Donkey.

'What use is that?' answered the caterpillar and continued to crawl on her way forwards.

'Please,' said the Blue Donkey. 'If you would only stop for a moment, I could make my way past you carefully and easily.'

'Why should I?' replied the caterpillar and did not stop.

The Blue Donkey inched along slowly. 'In order,' she explained, 'not to be stepped on.'

The caterpillar suddenly swung to the left. She clambered up a leaf, paused and glared. 'Typical,' she muttered with the utmost contempt.

'Typical of what?' asked the Blue Donkey.

'Of donkeys. Big, bullying, beastly and brash.'

'Oh, now wait a minute.' The Blue Donkey was beginning to get angry. 'That isn't fair. All I did was make a polite request.'

'And when I failed to comply, backed it with a threat.'

'What threat?' shouted the Blue Donkey, who was feeling thoroughly nettled by now. She had thrust her face close to the caterpillar and her breath was making the leaf tremble. The caterpillar was hanging on.

'Do you seriously wish to discuss the matter?' the caterpillar asked in a reasonable voice.

'Yes!'

'Then don't you see that from my point of view donkeys are a wholly unnecessary and dangerous encumbrance on the face of the planet?'

'But I can't help being big. As for being beastly, well, I am a beast. That is my nature.'

'Precisely,' murmured the caterpillar.

The Blue Donkey pulled herself together. 'But then can't you see that from my point of view caterpillars are a wholly unnecessary nuisance?'

'We are not,' replied the caterpillar firmly. 'And in any case we undergo a transformation.'

'Be reasonable,' pleaded the Blue Donkey. 'If you had your way, you'd abolish donkeys. But consider, what harm do I do by going about my business?'

'You crush caterpillars.'

'But I didn't!' cried the Blue Donkey.

'But you nearly did,' retorted the caterpillar.

'Is there no way then that we can be friends?' asked the Blue Donkey sadly.

'Not until you change.' The caterpillar was adamant.

'What must I do?'

'I don't know.' The caterpillar shrugged. 'Grow wings. Meditate hard. Alter your nature. That's your problem.'

The Blue Donkey turned away slowly. Her flank grazed the bush on which the caterpillar sat, but she didn't notice. She felt useless, hopeless and utterly snubbed. Behind her the caterpillar fell with a small plop.

Thunder and Lightning

'Let's face it,' the Blue Donkey said to her friend, Suniti. 'The donkey is not a heroic beast.'

'What?' asked Suniti.

'Donkeys – not heroic.'

'Why not?' enquired Suniti.

The Blue Donkey was taken aback. She thought she had been stating an incontrovertible fact. 'Because,' she replied, 'donkeys, by definition, are not heroic. It's – it's not in our nature.'

'I knew a Heroic Donkey once,' Suniti murmured.

'What! Tell me about her. What did she do?'

'First, she didn't kill anyone.'

The Blue Donkey looked most disappointed, but Suniti continued. 'Next, she did not enslave anyone.' By now the Blue Donkey was pawing the ground. Suniti hurried on, 'And finally, she did not exploit anyone.'

'Yes. But what did she do?'

'She lived.'

The Blue Donkey shook her head. 'No, that won't do. You've just described an ordinary donkey.'

'Let's not quibble,' said Suniti peaceably. 'Surely you'll admit that ordinary donkeys are pretty nice.'

'Oh, I knew that,' the Blue Donkey agreed, but she sounded dissatisfied.

'All right, I'll tell you an entirely different story,' offered Suniti. 'Once upon a time there was a Heroic Donkey whose mane grazed the heavens whenever she stood up, whose polished black hooves sparked thunder and lightning when she rampaged about, and whose trumpet-like braying hit the moon and bounced right back.'

The Blue Donkey was looking astonished. Suniti smiled. 'There. What do you think of her?' she asked.

'Noisy beast,' replied the Blue Donkey. Then she smiled back.

Nocturne

The Blue Donkey settled in the moonlight. It was all right, she told herself, donkeys had slept in the moonlight before – in Shakespeare, for example. Besides, there was no one about, so that if she felt a trifle self-conscious, what did it matter? Owls hooted, a tree creaked. No Titania came to pronounce the Blue Donkey not only beautiful, but also beloved – and that, perhaps, was just as well. With or without external validation, the Blue Donkey slept. She could not, of course, see herself sleep, any more than she could hear herself snore. Had she been awake and had anybody asked, she'd have said carefully that she saw herself as an ordinary creature. But nobody asked, and as for the donkey, she was fast asleep with the moonlight flung across her like a useless protection.